Sanjeev Kapoor's

Tasty Eating
for Healthy Living

In association with Alyona Kapoor

- Volume Five -

PopulaR
prakashan
www.popularprakashan.com

Published by:

POPULAR PRAKASHAN PVT. LTD.

301, Mahalaxmi Chambers

22, Bhulabhai Desai Road

Mumbai 400 026

for **KHANA KHAZANA PUBLICATIONS PVT. LTD.**

(4305)

ISBN – 978-81-7991-557-8

Nutritionist: Kirti Masurkar

Book Design: Pratibha Gurnani Creative

Photography: Bharat Bhirangi, Alim Bolar

Food Stylist: Anupa Das

Printed in India

Standard Press (India) Pvt. Ltd.,

34G, Poothayammal Nagar,

Near YRTV School, Sivakasi - 626 123.

contents

meet mr. sharma!

Kishen Sharma is a 49-year-old who has recently been diagnosed with diabetes. He has lived in Kota for twenty years and has a consultation with a diabetes specialist, dietician Jayshree for advice on his eating plan.

Sharma is approximately 15 kilograms overweight. He takes medicines to control his blood pressure but fortunately has no evidence of coronary heart disease or any family history of diabetes.

Sharma admits he is not very physically active and his exercise consists of about two hours of walking around his bungalow per week.

When Jayshree asks him to jot down what he eats in a typical day, he reveals the following:

Breakfast: 3-4 slices white bread, with butter, 1 - 1½ cups tea with full cream milk and a teaspoon sugar, sometimes a *kachori* or *samosa* bought from the shop around the corner.

Lunch: 4 *rotis* with ghee, 2 *katoris dal* with tempering of ghee, 1 *katori* green vegetable with evident oil and 1 *katori* chopped onion and tomato as a small salad and a piece of *mithai* for dessert.

Mid-afternoon: 1 cup tea with full cream milk and sugar and 4-5 sweet biscuits.

Dinner: 2 *katoris* or more pulao with vegetables or *gatta*, 1-2 *rotis* with ghee, 1-2 *katoris* vegetable curry with evident oil, 1 teaspoon pickle and 1 *katori dal* with tempering of ghee.

Post dinner: 1 fruit like apple or banana and one piece *mithai* (could be *ghevar, laddoo* or *barfi!*)

Some diet changes suggested by Jayshree:

Breakfast: 200 ml oats porridge made with skimmed milk, 1 slice brown bread with no butter, 1 cup tea with skimmed milk and no sugar, 1 apple.

Mid-morning: 1 glass thin buttermilk, 2 digestive biscuits.

Lunch: 2 *rotis* without ghee, 2 *katoris* thin *dal* with tempering of olive oil, 2 *katoris* lightly sautèed green vegetables or leafy vegetable cooked in a few drops of oil, 1 *katori* skimmed milk yogurt, 2 *katoris* chopped salad with no-oil dressing.

Mid-afternoon: 1 cup tea with skimmed milk and no sugar, 4-5 unsalted almonds.

Dinner: 1 *katori* brown rice *pulao* or *khichdi* cooked with one teaspoon oil, 1 *roti* without ghee, 2 *katoris* vegetable preparation with little gravy and 1 *katori* thin *dal* with no tempering, 1 teaspoon green chutney.

Post dinner: 1 piece of fruit.

Now Kishen Sharma's daily diet includes far more fibre, more of calcium-rich dairy foods, and plenty of complex carbohydrates like oats, nuts and at least five fruit and vegetable portions. He is eating fewer carbohydrates as a result of choosing smaller portion sizes of starchy foods like rice and *rotis*. He is losing weight slowly but steadily. He is a little more active as he goes for a thirty-minute walk four times a week. Even Mrs. Sharma and the two children are more energetic as the overall diet of the family has improved.

what jayshree told the sharmas

Jayshree did a smart thing. She advised both Mr. and Mrs. Sharma. She was of the opinion that if the parents ate healthy, the children would too! After evaluating Sharma's diet plan, she explained the importance of diet and lifestyle changes.

❶ Jayshree advised them to switch from white (bread, rice) to brown (bread, rice). Mrs. Sharma agreed though she has her doubts about how the children will adjust to the change in taste and texture. Jayshree tells her to make *khichdi* with brown rice and *dal* and add turmeric so that the children are unable to make out the difference.

❷ She advised them to refrain from the *kachoris* and *samosas*. She explained the disadvantages of eating deep-fried foods sold on streets and how the oil is mostly reused and full of free radicals. She asked Mrs. Sharma to introduce shallow-fried snacks made with olive oil for the children and not to deprive them of tasty stuff!

❸ When Sharma raised the point that his new diet plan might not be filling enough for him Jayshree gently pointed out to the increase in portions of yogurt and salad.

❹ Changing over from full-fat to skimmed milk was not something that Mrs. Sharma looked happy about. Her contention was that she made enough homemade ghee from the cream to last a month! Jayshree told her that she could buy a small packet of cow's milk ghee for the use of the children. She revealed that skimmed milk had more calcium than full-cream milk.

❺ The Sharmas were asked to aim for at least five portions of fruit and vegetables every day, but the children are fussy eaters. Jayshree advised her to make stuffed *paranthas* for the children using vegetable mixes or to give them fruits as a snack when they asked for biscuits.

❻ Mrs. Sharma was advised to change to non-stick cookware. She was also asked not to overcook vegetables as far as possible.

❼ Mrs. Sharma was of the opinion that a little ghee was good for health. Jayshree pointed out the use of olive oil and inclusion of yogurt and nuts in Sharma's new diet plan.

The Sharmas are now more confident of making healthy eating a way of life for their family.

alads

gajar, kishmish and black olive salad

Ingredients

4-5 large carrots
½ cup raisins
6-8 black olives, sliced
2 tablespoons lemon juice
5-6 black peppercorns, crushed
1 green chilli, finely chopped
1 tablespoon honey
Salt to taste
¼ teaspoon black salt
6 walnut kernels, crushed
1 teaspoon extra virgin olive oil
6- 8 fresh mint leaves

Method

❶ Thickly grate the carrots. Refrigerate till required for use.

❷ Combine the lemon juice, peppercorns, green chilli, honey, salt, black salt, walnuts, raisins, black olives and extra virgin olive oil to make a dressing.

❸ Just before serving, add the dressing to the grated carrots and toss. Serve garnished with mint leaves.

Low in calories but high in carbohydrates, antioxidants and omega-3 fatty acids... have a bowlful of this salad when you need perk-me-up food. It is also excellent for the skin.

rojak

Ingredients

½ fresh pineapple, cut into ½-inch cubes
1 small yam, cut into ½-inch cubes and boiled
1 cucumber, cut into ½-inch cubes
3 tablespoons brown sugar
¼ cup tamarind juice
3 fresh red chillies, seeded and chopped

Method

❶ Mix the brown sugar, tamarind juice and red chillies.

❷ Place the pineapple, yam and cucumber in a bowl. Add the dressing and toss well.

❸ Serve.

This salad with its varied textures is a pleasant addition to my planned healthy menus. This wonderful blend of vegetables and fruits is a popular street food in Malaysia where it is sold in many other variations.

murgh aur shimla mirch salad

Ingredients

2 boneless chicken breasts, skinned
1 medium red capsicum, seeded and cut into strips
1 medium green capsicum, seeded and cut into strips
1 medium yellow capsicum, seeded and cut into strips
5-6 green olives
5-6 black olives

Marinade

1 tablespoon olive oil
3 tablespoons skimmed milk yogurt
½ tablespoon green chilli paste
1 teaspoon ginger-garlic paste
½ teaspoon *garam masala* powder
5-6 black peppercorns, crushed
Salt to taste

Dressing

4 teaspoons extra virgin olive oil
2 teaspoons lemon juice
2 teaspoons *chaat masala*
Black salt to taste

Method

❶ Mix all the ingredients for the marinade in a bowl. Add the chicken breasts and marinate for an hour preferably in a refrigerator.

❷ Mix all the ingredients for the dressing and set aside.

❸ Grill the chicken breasts on a pre-heated grill, or on a *tawa* on medium heat, for eight to ten minutes or until done, turning once or twice and taking care they remain juicy. Allow to cool and cut into one-inch pieces. Transfer to a bowl.

❹ Add the capsicums, olives and the dressing. Toss lightly and serve immediately.

Grilled chicken in a tangy dressing with crisp capsicums: I could make a meal of this high-protein salad!

marinated prawn salad

Ingredients

15 medium prawns, cleaned and blanched
¼ cup grated coconut
4 shallots, sliced
2 lemon grass stalks, chopped
3 Kaffir lime leaves, finely shredded
A few fresh mint leaves, to garnish

Dressing
A pinch of brown sugar
4 tablespoons lemon juice
1 tablespoon fish sauce
2 fresh red chillies, chopped
1 garlic clove, chopped
Salt to taste

Method

❶ In a large bowl, toss together the prawns, coconut, shallots, lemon grass and lime leaves.

❷ For the dressing, mix together the brown sugar, lemon juice, fish sauce, red chillies, garlic and salt in a small bowl.

❸ Pour the dressing over the prawn and coconut mixture and toss gently to mix.

❹ Serve, garnished with fresh mint leaves.

Prawns contain vitamins that enhance the health of the skin, bones and teeth. In this lightly cooked form, they add crunch and flavour marrying well with the lime leaves and mint.

chilled melon ball salad

Ingredients

¼ watermelon
1 medium muskmelon

Dressing
1½ teaspoons lemon juice
2 tablespoons orange juice
3-4 black peppercorns, crushed
1 tablespoon roughly torn fresh mint
Salt to taste
Black salt to taste

Method

❶ Using a Parisienne scoop (melon baller) scoop out small balls from the watermelon. Discard all the seeds.

❷ Cut the muskmelon in half. Scoop out small balls fromthe centre, leaving a thick shell. Discard all the seeds. Reserve the melon shells.

❸ Place the melon balls in a refrigerator to chill thoroughly.

❹ Mix together all the ingredients for the dressing. Pour over the melon balls and toss gently once or twice to mix. Spoon into the melon shells and serve immediately.

Chef's Tip: The melon shells can be given a decorative zigzag edge using a small sharp knife.

Melons are a good source of potassium, iron and many trace minerals. The salad also provides Vitamin C. This salad can be had by all - pregnant women, adolescents and weight-watchers.

caesar salad

Ingredients

2 thick slices of bread
1 tablespoon olive oil
2 garlic cloves, peeled and roughly crushed
½ head of iceberg lettuce
½ head of lollo rosso lettuce
5-6 basil leaves
100 grams Parmesan cheese

Dressing

2 eggs
1 teaspoon French mustard paste
1 teaspoon Worcestershire sauce
2 tablespoons extra virgin olive oil
Salt to taste
3-4 black peppercorns, crushed

Method

❶ Cut the bread slices into one-inch pieces.

❷ Heat one tablespoon oil in a pan and add the garlic. Add the bread cubes and sauté till they are a little crisp and browned at the edges. Remove and set aside.

❸ Boil sufficient water in a pan, add the eggs and boil them for two to three minutes only.

❹ Wash and tear the lettuce leaves and keep them in a big bowl. Tear the basil leaves and add to the lettuce. Add the bread pieces with the garlic and toss lightly. Make cheese shavings using a peeler or grate the cheese and add it to the bowl.

❺ Break the lightly boiled eggs into another bowl and whisk well. Add the mustard paste, Worcestershire sauce, olive oil, salt and freshly crushed black peppercorns and whisk till well blended.

❻ Add the dressing to the salad and toss lightly. Serve immediately.

You may come across different versions of Caesar Salad in various hotels and restaurants. This is my favourite and was served in my friend's restaurant in Wellington, New Zealand. I can suggest that you use brown bread instead of white bread in this salad. It adds more fibre to the whole bowl with the lettuce too providing roughage.

bread salad with diced chicken

Ingredients

3-inch piece of French loaf, cut into small cubes
2 boneless chicken breasts, skinned, boiled and cut into small cubes
2 tablespoons olive oil
1 tablespoon vinegar
2-3 garlic cloves
½ cup fresh basil leaves + a few for garnish
Salt to taste
2 medium tomatoes, seeded and cut into small pieces
1 large cucumber, seeded and cut into small pieces
4 lettuce leaves

Method

❶ Preheat an oven to 180°C/350°F/Gas Mark 4

❷ Spread the bread cubes in a shallow baking dish and bake in the preheated oven for ten minutes or until crisp and golden. Remove from the oven and set aside.

❸ Combine the olive oil, vinegar, garlic, basil leaves and salt in a food processor and blend at high speed for a few seconds to make a coarse paste. Transfer to a large bowl.

❹ Add the bread cubes, chicken, tomatoes and cucumber and toss well. Let the salad stand for five minutes. This allows the bread to soften slightly.

❺ Line a serving dish with lettuce leaves and transfer the salad into it. Garnish with basil leaves and serve immediately.

Basil leaves have been revered since ancient times as beneficial due to their medicinal properties. The leaves are anti-inflammatory and are recommended for people suffering from water retention. Basil, like other herbs, can be used as a flavouring agent in a salt-free diet.

summer tomato pasta salad

Ingredients

10-12 cherry tomatoes, halved
1½ cups penne (quill-shaped pasta)
Salt to taste
¼ medium broccoli, separated into small florets
½ teaspoon sugar
10-12 black peppercorns
2 tablespoons olive oil
15-20 basil leaves
150 grams skimmed milk cottage cheese, cut into 2-inch long strips
1 tablespoon vinegar
1 teaspoon caster sugar
2 tablespoons pine nuts/walnuts (optional)

Method

❶ Cook the penne in five to six cups of boiling salted water till *al dente* (cooked but still firm to the bite). Drain, refresh and spread on a large plate to cool.

❷ Boil the broccoli with salt and sugar for two to three minutes. Drain, refresh and set it aside.

❸ Crush the black peppercorns with one tablespoon olive oil and fifteen basil leaves with a mortar and pestle. Add the remaining olive oil to this paste.

❹ In a large bowl combine the pasta, cherry tomatoes, broccoli, cottage cheese strips, prepared paste, vinegar, caster sugar and salt. Toss well to mix.

❺ Transfer the salad onto a serving dish, garnish with the remaining basil leaves and pinenuts/walnuts and serve immediately.

Note: You can also use large tomatoes cut into quarters in place of cherry tomatoes.

They say eat with your eyes first. This salad qualifies! With the white of the pasta, the red tomato and the green broccoli... it is a pleasant sight to behold. The cottage cheese is an Indian touch I just could not resist!

cottage cheese and pineapple salad

Ingredients

300 grams skimmed milk cottage cheese,
cut into ½-inch cubes

½ small fresh pineapple, cut into ½-inch cubes

1 large unpeeled cucumber, cut into 1-inch pieces

1 medium green capsicum, cut into 1-inch pieces

½ small head of iceberg lettuce

6-8 black olives, stoned and sliced

1 teaspoon garlic paste

1 tablespoon lemon juice

1 teaspoon red chilli powder

½ teaspoon mixed dried herbs

Salt to taste

1½ tablespoons oil

Dressing

1½ tablespoons salad oil

4 tablespoons vinegar

1 teaspoon sugar

1 teaspoon mustard powder

5-6 black peppercorns, crushed

½ teaspoon white pepper powder

Method

❶ Combine the garlic paste, lemon juice, chilli powder, dried herbs and salt. Rub the mixture into the cottage cheese pieces and set aside to marinate, preferably in a refrigerator, for fifteen to twenty minutes.

❷ Mix together all the ingredients for the dressing in a bowl.

❸ Thread the cottage cheese cubes onto skewers. Heat the oil on a griddle and place the skewers on it. Cook, turning the skewers a few times, to brown the cottage cheese evenly on all sides. Remove the cottage cheese pieces off the skewers and transfer onto a plate and set aside to cool.

❹ Combine the grilled cottage cheese, pineapple, cucumber, capsicum, roughly torn iceberg lettuce and olives in a large serving bowl. Drizzle the dressing over and toss to mix well. Serve immediately.

A healthy bowlful indeed! Low-fat cottage cheese is a good source of protein and blends well with other raw veggies. Pineapple, cucumber and capsicum are all low in calories whereas the olives add essential omega-3 fatty acids.

vegetable ribbons

Ingredients

1 medium zucchini, trimmed
2 medium carrots, trimmed
2 medium cucumbers, trimmed
Salt to taste
5 medium black olives, sliced

Dressing
2 tablespoons vinegar
1 tablespoon soy sauce
1 teaspoon brown sugar
¼ teaspoon red chilli flakes
3-4 fresh basil leaves, roughly torn
Salt to taste

Method

❶ Cut the zucchini, carrots and cucumbers lengthways into thin ribbons with a potato peeler or a manual slicer. Sprinkle a little salt and set aside for five minutes.

❷ Process the vinegar, soy sauce, brown sugar, chilli flakes, basil leaves and salt to a coarse paste in a blender. Transfer to a bowl.

❸ Squeeze the cut vegetables to remove excess liquid.

❹ Add the vegetables to the dressing in the bowl and toss well.

❺ Serve, garnished with olive slices.

Chef's Tip: Serve immediately as the zucchini tends to become soggy.

This salad is high in potassium, a very important nutrient for people suffering from high blood pressure, heart disease or the effects of menopause. Consuming raw vegetables increases the Basal Metabolic Rate (BMR) and helps in weight loss. Olives are a good source of antioxidants.

beverages

black grape sherbet

Ingredients

4 cups black grape juice
¾ teaspoon cumin seeds
½ teaspoon carom seeds
1 teaspoon fennel seeds
3 teaspoons black salt
1½ tablespoons tamarind pulp
Crushed ice

Method

❶ Dry-roast the cumin seeds, carom seeds and fennel seeds and grind with the black salt to a fine powder.

❷ Pour the black grape juice into a jug; add the ground spices and tamarind pulp and mix well.

❸ Add the crushed ice and mix. Pour into individual glasses and serve chilled.

Black grapes are nutrient-dense because they contain potassium, phosphorus and Vitamin C. Seeds like cumin and fennel are good appetizing agents and the tamarind adds some sour notes to the overall sweetness, making the sherbet more palatable.

shikanji

Ingredients

12 tablespoons lemon juice
Salt to taste
4 teaspoons black salt
10 teaspoons powdered sugar
2 teaspoons darkly roasted cumin powder
1 teaspoon black pepper powder
4 cups club soda
4 fresh mint sprigs
Ice cubes as required

Method

❶ Combine the lemon juice with salt, black salt, powdered sugar, roasted cumin powder and pepper powder in a bowl.

❷ Pour equal quantities of the mixture into individual tall glasses. Top each up with club soda and ice cubes.

❸ Decorate with the mint sprigs and serve chilled.

When you need a drink that cools you and whets the appetite, *shikanji* is the answer. I have added a contemporary touch with the club soda to make it more attractive for the 'burger-cola' brigade. There is Vitamin-C-rich lemon juice and cooling *jeera* and mint... making it healthy as well!

strawberry and orange soya shake

Ingredients

4 tablespoons strawberry crush
1 orange
6 tablespoons orange squash
4 cups chilled soya milk
4 teaspoons sugar
4 scoops vanilla ice cream
2 cups crushed ice

Method

❶ Peel and remove the pith from the orange segments. Peel off the white membrane and separate the flakes. Place in the refrigerator to chill for ten minutes.

❷ Place the strawberry crush, orange squash, soya milk, sugar and vanilla ice cream in a blender and process till smooth.

❸ Place the crushed ice in four glasses. Pour the strawberry -soya shake over the ice.

❹ Top with the orange flakes and serve immediately.

I simply adore this lovely-looking milk shake and have it very often for breakfast. Soya is rich in good quality protein. Oranges and strawberries are rich in minerals, vitamins and fibre. A power drink that keeps one going through the rigours of a busy day.

party punch

Ingredients

4 tablespoons rose syrup
2 cups orange juice
2 cups mango juice
4 scoops vanilla ice cream
1 cup ice cubes

Method

❶ Pour one tablespoon rose syrup in each glass and swirl to form a design. Refrigerate.

❷ Process the orange juice, mango juice and vanilla ice cream along with the ice cubes in a blender till smooth.

❸ Pour the prepared punch into the rose syrup-lined glasses and serve immediately.

A colourful drink that is not only pleasing to look at but also rich in Vitamin A.

kahwa tea

Ingredients

1 teaspoon *kahwa* tea leaves, crushed
2 green cardamoms
2 inches cinnamon
3 teaspoons sugar
2-3 saffron threads (optional)
4-5 almonds, finely crushed

Method

❶ Pound the cardamoms and cinnamon to a powder.

❷ Pour three cups of water into a pan; add the crushed *kahwa* tea leaves, cardamom-cinnamon powder, sugar and saffron and bring to a boil.

❸ Boil for five to six minutes or till the tea turns a pale gold.

❹ Strain into individual teacups.

❺ Sprinkle the almonds on top and serve hot.

Kahwa Tea is a modification of normal tea. The blend of spices helps to increase the Basal Metabolic Rate (BMR). It is a low-calorie drink for weight-watchers if the sugar is substituted with an artificial sweetener. Almonds add some antioxidants and some protein to the tea.

moroccan mint tea

Ingredients

2 teaspoons tea leaves
16 fresh mint leaves
4 lemons, cut into wedges
2 inches cinnamon
4 star anise
16 teaspoons caster sugar

Method

❶ Place the tea leaves, mint leaves, lemon wedges, cinnamon, star anise and caster sugar in a teapot.

❷ Pour boiling water into the teapot, cover and allow to infuse for about three to four minutes.

❸ Stir well to dissolve the sugar.

❹ Pour into individual glasses and serve hot.

Ever wondered why mint is considered so beneficial for health? Because it contains plenty of vitamins and minerals which improve digestion and provide relief during asthmatic attacks. Lemon is a good source of Vitamin C.

melon and mango smoothie

Ingredients

1 medium ripe musk melon
2 ripe Alphonso mangoes
2 tablespoons strawberry crush
1 cup crushed ice

Method

❶ Cut the melon into wedges, peel and remove the seeds. Chop half a wedge into half-inch cubes. Chop the remaining melon into one-inch cubes. Place in a freezer for three hours.

❷ Peel the mangoes and chop one slice into half-inch cubes. Chop the remaining mango into one-inch cubes. Place in a freezer for three hours.

❸ Place the larger cubes of melon and mango in a blender with the strawberry crush and one cup of crushed ice. Blend till smooth and frothy.

❹ Pour into individual glasses and serve, topped with the smaller melon and mango cubes.

I just cannot let the summer months go by without this exotic smoothie. Melons and mangoes make great partners here, for whereas the former is rich in Vitamin A, the latter provides carotenoids. Added to that are the strawberries which are high in potassium and are low in calories. A drink that can be had anytime.

mango smoothie

Ingredients

3 large ripe mangoes, peeled and chopped
1 medium ripe mango,
cut into ½-inch cubes, to garnish
3 cups chilled skimmed milk
6 tablespoons chilled skimmed milk yogurt
8 tablespoons sugar
10-12 ice cubes, crushed

Method

❶ Place the chopped mangoes in the freezer for a while.

❷ Process the chilled mangoes, milk, yogurt, sugar and crushed ice cubes together in a blender.

❸ Carefully pour the mixture into individual glasses.

❹ Serve chilled, decorated with the mango cubes.

Mango is the king of fruits and adds grandeur to the table in summer. It is a rich source of Vitamin A and should be eaten by growing children. I have used skimmed milk yogurt as it has higher levels of calcium and lower levels of fat than regular full-cream milk.

kokum and anar slush

Ingredients

1⅓ cups *kokum* syrup
4 tablespoons pomegranate kernels
2 teaspoons roasted cumin powder
2 teaspoons black salt
8 tablespoons sugar
4 cups crushed ice

Method

❶ Process the *kokum* syrup, roasted cumin powder, black salt, sugar and crushed ice in a smoothie maker until slushy.

❷ Pour into individual glasses and serve, decorated with a sprinkling of the pomegranate kernels.

Pomegranate, with its appealing colour, when juiced, is a favourite with health freaks as the juice has antioxidants, vitamins, potassium, folic acid and iron. The cocktail/mocktail circuit makes excellent use of grenadine which is thickened and sweetened pomegranate juice. Here pomegranate kernels add visual appeal and texture to the cooling and appetite-whetting *kokum* slush.

coconut refresher

Ingredients

2 whole tender coconuts
2 apples, peeled and cored
8 tablespoons sugar syrup
2 tablespoons lemon juice
4 apple fans for garnishing

Method

❶ Chill the whole tender coconuts thoroughly. Slice off the tops, drain the water and scoop out the flesh.

❷ Chop the apples roughly. Process the coconut water with the coconut flesh, apples, sugar syrup and lemon juice in a blender until smooth.

❸ Pour into individual glasses. Decorate with the apple fans and serve chilled.

Tender coconut water is a natural, safe and hygienic drink recommended for maintaining electrolyte balance and is also a good aid to treat dehydration. Apples are rich in pectin, an insoluble fibre, which aids in digestion.

tackling health issues

Lifestyle diseases and other health conditions can be managed by eating
a healthy natural diet and following an exercise regime. It is therefore important
to know how one can modify one's diet and lifestyle to manage these
diseases and conditions.

diabetes

❶ Be active. A person who is active can keep a watch on his weight and with that also keep a check on increasing sugar levels. Physical activity lowers sugar levels and increases insulin sensitivity.

❷ Consume plenty of fibre. Foods high in fibre include fruits, vegetables, beans, whole grains, nuts and seeds. Fibre is roughage and controls the blood sugar levels.

❸ Eat whole grains. Whole grains can reduce risk of diabetes and maintain the sugar levels. Replace refined foods with whole and unrefined foods e.g. white breads, made with refined flour can be replaced by multi-grain breads and mixed flour.

❹ Keep a check on your weight. An ideal weight improves overall health. Diabetics need a balance of diet and exercise.

❺ Make healthier choices and avoid fad diets. Excessive fats are a strict no-no. You must have small quantities of fat for absorption of fat-soluble vitamins. Olive oil is a good choice.

❻ Say no to excess salt. Adding salt at the table should be avoided. Try pepper or other herbs and spices.

❼ Avoid artificial sweeteners. Our body's need for sugar is fulfilled by naturally-available sugars in foods, so as far as possible avoid artificial sweeteners.

❽ Reduce intake of red meat. Lean more towards a vegetarian diet. Eggs and fish should be eaten thrice a week.

❾ Choose the correct foods. Some foods help in controlling the blood sugar levels - bitter gourds (*karele*), fenugreek seeds (*methi dana*), Indian black berry (*jamun*), garlic, flax seeds and cinnamon help in lowering the blood sugar.

obesity

❶ Avoid fats. Eat low-fat foods. Olive oil is a good cooking medium.

❷ Choose roasted and steamed foods over deep-fried foods

❸ Plan a low-calorie diet, which prevents calories from accumulating in the form of fat.

❹ Eat complex carbohydrates like whole grain foods, fruits and vegetables. They also add fibre to the diet.

❺ Eat good-quality protein as it helps keep muscles fit and toned.

❻ Drink plenty of water, and have fluids like soups and vegetable juices.

❼ Exercise regularly.

❽ Avoid stress and have a good sleep.

❾ Choose the correct foods. Examples: beans, nuts, low-fat dairy products, citrus fruits and green vegetables.

heart disease

❶ Have green leafy vegetables like spinach and broccoli.

❷ Have more of foods with both soluble fibre and insoluble fibre. Vegetables are a good source.

❸ Have fruits like apples, grapes, oranges, strawberries, papaya, mango, banana, kiwi, *amla* and apricots.

❹ Have vegetables rich in carotenoids. Examples: carrots, pumpkins and tomatoes.

❺ Have beans as they are a rich source of proteins. Soya beans and tofu help to reduce the 'bad cholesterol' and thereby reduce the risk of heart disease.

❻ Have green tea as it contains polyphenols which reduce the risk of heart disease.

❼ Have salmon as it is high in omega-3 fatty acids. It lowers LDL or the 'bad cholesterol'.

anaemia

❶ Include cauliflower greens, leaves of beetroot and radish in vegetable preparations.

❷ Include liver, lean meats, fish and poultry in your diet.

❸ Include beans, whole grains, cereals, leafy vegetables, dried fruits and nuts in your diet.

digestive problems

Acidity

❶ Avoid erratic working hours. Erratic schedules or a lack of fixed routines play havoc with regular mealtimes, enhancing acidity.

❷ Avoid the wrong foods. Sudden hunger pangs can make anyone reach out for fast foods. These worsen acidity.

❸ Be active. Lack of physical activity leads to slower digestion of food.

❹ Be aware of the various types of foods. Ignorance about healthier alternatives aggravates the condition. Fried foods, biscuits and soft drinks, though easily available, are best avoided.

Learn about nutrition. One should at least have basic nutritional information of what one is eating.

Constipation

❶ Laxatives and enemas provide only a temporary solution.

❷ Plan a high-fibre diet. Include fruits, vegetables and whole grains in your diet for easy bowel movement.

❸ Avoid spicy and deep-fried foods.

Acidic And Alkaline Foods

Acidic: Corn, meat, fish, eggs, coffee, beans, most grains, white rice, bread, pasta, plums, prunes, buttermilk, sour cream, pickles, ketchups and mayonnaise. If you have increasing levels of acidity, avoid these foods.

Alkaline: Bananas, milk, chocolates, figs, orange juice, potatoes, spinach, watermelon, mineral water, cabbage, carrots, beetroots, almonds, raisins, olives, avocados and natural sugar. These foods relieve acidity.

thyroid problems

Hyperthyroid

When the thyroid gland is over-active it is said to be hyperthyroid. People suffering from hyperthyroidism tend to lose weight because their body's metabolic rate is higher than normal.

❶ Use fats and sugar sparingly.

❷ Add fibre to the diet.

❸ Till the hyperthyroid condition is stabilized eat a high-protein diet.

Hypothyroid

When the thyroid gland is under-active it is said to be hypothyroid. Since the condition usually involves weight gain it is advisable to follow a weight-loss diet.

❶ Have natural foods, whole grains, lots of fruits and vegetables, seafood and other lean proteins and nuts.

❷ Consume high-fibre foods. They help in losing weight as they give a feeling of fullness.

❸ Beans, whole grains and their products like oatmeal and muesli have plenty of fibre.

❹ Frequent small meals are recommended. Mini-meals will help to increase the metabolism that alters in hypothyroid patients. One should keep these meals around 300 calories, so that weight reduction is also possible.

❺ Water intake should be increased.

❻ Avoid cabbage, cauliflower, kale, spinach, peaches, pears and radishes as they aggravate goitre.

excessive cholesterol

❶ Include beans in all forms: dry, cooked and canned. Also have lentils and peas. These are low in fat and have a low glycemic index.

❷ Have all soya products, soya granules, milk, nuggets, and tofu. They are rich in dietary fibre and protective nutrients including minerals and B vitamins.

❸ Adopt olive oil. Olive oil is rich in monounsaturated fatty acids and Vitamin E. Olive and its products promote the reduction of bad cholesterol and increase of good cholesterol.

❹ Have fat-free or low-fat dairy products. Low-fat milk, fat-free milk and skimmed milk yogurt

are high in calcium, which is essential for the smooth functioning of the heart and prevention of osteoporosis.

❺ Have natural antioxidants. Fruits and vegetables help to lower cholesterol levels, but particularly Vitamin C and beta-carotene are more helpful. Vitamin C-rich foods include all citrus fruits, berries, guavas, the entire cabbage family as well as capsicums. Beta-carotene-rich foods include dark yellow orange fruits and vegetables, and all green leafy vegetables.

❻ Have garlic and other members of Allium family like spring onions and onion.

❼ Whole foods and fibre are essential. Whole grains, unsifted flour and unprocessed grains are rich in Vitamin B, minerals and dietary fibre and low in fat and cholesterol. Eat oats or muesli daily to keep a check on the cholesterol.

❽ Omega-3 is helpful. People who eat omega-3-rich fish three or more times a week are at a lower risk of heart disease. The best fish are salmon, tuna, trout and sardines. Other foods rich in omega-3 fatty acids are flax seeds, walnuts and eggs.

❾ Fenugreek seeds can help. Have them either powdered or soaked or have sprouted fenugreek seeds.

esserts

eggless pineapple mousse

Ingredients

6 slices canned pineapple, at room temperature
2 teaspoons unflavoured gelatine
½ tin (200 grams) sweetened condensed milk
3 teaspoons lemon juice
250 grams cream
A few drops pineapple essence
A few drops of edible yellow colour
1 tablespoon powdered sugar
Glacé cherries, as required

Method

❶ Mix the gelatine with half cup water in a small pan. Heat on low heat, stirring continuously, till it dissolves.

❷ Pour the condensed milk in a bowl and beat till light and creamy. In another bowl, mix the lemon juice with half a cup of pineapple syrup from the tin.

❸ Chop five slices of pineapple. Add the pineapple syrup and pineapple to the condensed milk.

❹ Pour the gelatine solution into the condensed milk mixture stirring continuously. Freeze the mixture for half an hour till it is thick.

❺ Remove from the freezer and beat till smooth. Add two hundred grams of cream and reserve the remaining cream for decoration.

❻ Add the pineapple essence and yellow colour, beat well and put it back in the freezer for fifteen to twenty minutes.

❼ Remove from the freezer and beat again till smooth. Pour into a serving dish and freeze for one hour or till set.

❽ Whip the reserved cream with powdered sugar.

❾ Remove the mousse from the freezer. Transfer the whipped cream in a piping bag fitted with a star nozzle and make rosettes on the surface of the mousse. Place a glacé cherry on each rosette and serve immediately.

Vegetarians have always missed out on mousse because of the presence of egg. However, my eggless recipe here is perfect for them. But if you are watching your waistline, this dessert is best reserved for those very special celebratory moments!

tiramisù

Ingredients

12 slices (175 grams) chocolate sponge cake
½ tablespoon unflavoured gelatine
1 cup thick cream
½ cup powdered sugar
3 egg yolks
¼ cup sugar
2 tablespoons + 2 teaspoons instant coffee powder
¾ cup mascarpone cheese
Chocolate curls, to decorate

Method

❶ Cut each slice of cake in half.

❷ Dissolve the gelatine in three tablespoons of hot water.

❸ Whip the cream with the powdered sugar till stiff and set aside.

❹ Whip the egg yolks with sugar and one tablespoon of water in a double boiler or in a heatproof bowl over a pan of simmering water, till the mixture forms thick ribbons. Set aside to cool.

❺ Mix two tablespoons of instant coffee powder in half a cup of water and soak the chocolate sponge fingers in the solution.

❻ Arrange half the sponge fingers in a layer at the base of a springform tin.

❼ Mix two teaspoons of instant coffee powder in one teaspoon of water. Add this along with the mascarpone cheese and gelatine to the egg mixture and mix well. Fold in the whipped cream.

❽ Pour half the mixture over the chocolate fingers. Arrange the remaining chocolate fingers over and top with the remaining mixture and level the top.

❾ Place it in the refrigerator till set.

❿ Remove from the tin, cut into wedges and serve chilled, decorated with chocolate curls.

It takes only a few essentials to get one of the most popular Italian desserts right. When literally translated it means 'pick me up' or to put it in a better way, 'make me happier'!

mango cheesecake

Ingredients

Crust
8-10 bran biscuits or digestive biscuits
4 tablespoons butter

Filling
1 cup skimmed milk
½ cup condensed milk
1 tablespoon cornflour
1 tablespoon carrageenan (vegetarian gelatine)
1½ cups drained skimmed milk yogurt
2 cups skimmed milk cottage cheese
2 cups mango pulp
½ teaspoon mango essence
½ cup sugar, powdered

Topping
1 tablespoon mango jelly crystals
1 mango, chopped

Method

❶ For the crust, crush the biscuits to a coarse powder and place in a bowl. Add the butter and mix well. Place the mixture in a six-inch springform tin (loose bottom tin) lined with greaseproof paper. Press the mixture lightly and place in the refrigerator to set.

❷ For the filling, heat the milk in a pan. Add the condensed milk and mix. Mix the cornflour with a little milk and add it to the hot milk. Cook, stirring continuously, till the mixture thickens. Set aside.

❸ Mix the carrageenan in a little water and heat in the microwave for one minute. Remove from the microwave and set aside.

❹ Place the drained yogurt in a bowl. Add the cottage cheese and whisk well. Add the mango pulp and mix again. Add the mango essence and the milk mixture and mix again. Add the powdered sugar and blend with a hand blender. Add the dissolved carrageenan and blend again.

❺ Pour the mixture into the prepared tin over the biscuit layer. Refrigerate for two to three hours.

❻ For the topping, dissolve the mango jelly in a quarter cup of water, bring to a boil and cool.

❼ Spread a layer of mango jelly over the set cheesecake. Chill until the jelly sets.

❽ Remove from the springform tin and cut into eight wedges with a sharp knife dipped in hot water. Serve chilled decorated with chopped mango.

Chef's Tip: A springform tin is similar to a round shallow cake tin but with a removable base.

Cheesecake is something that does not require a lucky charm... contrary to popular belief! This recipe is a sure success and purely vegetarian. It has the added bonus of the king of fruits, mango!

mango bhapa doi with citrus fruits

Ingredients

1 tin (400 grams) condensed milk
1 cup thick skimmed milk yogurt, whisked
½ cup mango pulp
½ cup skimmed milk
A few peeled segments of orange
A few peeled segments of sweet lime
A few pomegranate kernels
A small sprig of fresh mint

Method

❶ Pour the condensed milk in a bowl. Add the yogurt, mango pulp and milk and mix well. Transfer the mixture into a steamer container.

❷ Heat sufficient water in a steamer. Cover the container with aluminium foil and place in the steamer.

❸ Cover the steamer and steam for twenty to twenty five minutes.

❹ Cool and place in the refrigerator to set.

❺ Unmould onto a serving plate. Arrange the orange and sweet lime segments in a decorative pattern all around. Top with a few pomegranate kernels. Place a small sprig of mint on top and serve chilled.

Simple and nice! I love making this in the mango season and the final colourful presentation always makes people smile. Mango is rich in Vitamin A and a complete meal when had with a glass of cold milk.

kesari indrayani

Ingredients

20-25 small *rasogollas*
2 litres (10 cups) skimmed milk
¾ cup sugar
A few threads of saffron
8-10 pistachios
½ cup fresh pomegranate kernels
¼ cup almonds, blanched and peeled

Method

❶ Blanch the pistachios in boiling water. Drain, refresh, peel and slice.

❷ Bring the milk to a boil, reduce the heat and simmer till the milk reduces to half its original volume.

❸ Add the sugar and saffron and cook till the sugar dissolves.

❹ Squeeze the *rasogollas* to remove excess syrup and place them in a bowl. Pour the milk-cream mixture over and set aside to cool. When completely cold, place in the refrigerator to chill.

❺ To serve, place a few chilled *rasogollas* in individual *kasoras* (earthenware bowls).

❻ Sprinkle pomegranate kernels, pistachios and almonds and serve chilled.

What I love about this dessert is that it looks and tastes superb and belies the simple method of preparation! Great to make when you have large numbers to entertain. For the health conscious the pomegranate used in this sweet dish not only makes it colourful but is also heart-healthy and proven to be good for glowing skin.

khajurachi wadi

Ingredients

½ kilogram dates, seeded and chopped
2 tablespoons pure ghee
1 tablespoon gum resin, crushed
¼ cup cashew nuts and pistachios
½ cup almonds
1 tablespoon poppy seeds, roasted
1 teaspoon green cardamom powder
½ teaspoon nutmeg powder
Aluminium foil as required

Method

❶ Coarsely grind the dates in a mixer and transfer to a bowl. Coarsely grind cashew nuts, pistachios and almonds.

❷ Heat one tablespoon of ghee in a pan, add the gum resin and fry till golden brown. Remove and set aside.

❸ To the same pan, add the remaining ghee and sauté the coarsely ground dried fruits and poppy seeds. Add the dates and mix well. Sauté till the dates are heated through.

❹ Remove onto a plate and set aside to cool slightly.

❺ Add the cardamom powder and nutmeg powder. Crush the gum resin and add. Mix everything well and knead into a dough.

❻ Divide the mixture into two to three portions and shape into cylinders. Wrap in aluminium foil and refrigerate for four to five hours.

❼ Just before serving, unwrap the rolls and cut them into half-inch thick rounds.

Gum resin (*gond*) is very high in calcium, essential fatty acids, iron, folate and Vitamin B. It acts as a galactagogue and therefore beneficial for lactating women. It is also beneficial for the elderly.

chocolate and bean curd mousse

Ingredients

300 grams dark cooking chocolate, grated
200 grams silken bean curd (tofu)
1 cup low-fat cream
¾ cup whipped cream
5 teaspoons sugar
Cocoa powder for sprinkling

Method

❶ Melt the dark chocolate in the microwave oven for one minute. Purée the bean curd with half a cup of water. Whisk the chocolate till smooth, add the low-fat cream and whisk again. Add the bean curd purée and mix.

❷ Add the whipped cream and sugar and mix well.

❸ Transfer into individual bowls. Sprinkle a little cocoa powder through a sieve. Chill in the refrigerator and serve.

Mousse is quite a popular dessert and bean curd adds to its goodness. Bean curd or tofu is especially rich in protein, unsaturated fats, calcium and iron. The intake of tofu reduces menopausal symptoms, risk of coronary heart disease and osteoporosis.

chocolate chip cookies

Ingredients

¾ cup chocolate chips
60 grams low-fat butter
1 egg white
½ teaspoon vanilla essence
½ cup wholewheat flour
¼ cup refined flour
½ teaspoon soda bicarbonate
¼ teaspoon salt
5 teaspoons sugar
½ cup coarsely crushed walnut kernels

Method

❶ Preheat an oven to 180°C/350°F/Gas Mark 4. Grease a baking tray.

❷ Place the butter in a bowl and cream it. Add the egg white and vanilla essence and continue to cream for some time. Set aside.

❸ In a separate bowl, sift together both the flour, soda bicarbonate and salt, fold into the butter mixture and mix well.

❹ Add the sugar, walnuts and chocolate chips, reserving a few chocolate chips and mix.

❺ Divide the dough into twelve equal portions and shape each into a round cookie.

❻ Place the cookies on the greased baking tray keeping enough distance between each. Sprinkle the remaining chocolate chips on top and bake in the preheated oven for twenty to twenty-five minutes.

❼ Remove onto a wire rack to cool before serving or store in an airtight container.

The oh-so-popular *Chocolate Chip Cookies*, if made with low fat butter and wholewheat flour, are transformed into a healthy snack since they provide nutrition. Walnuts are heart-healthy and result in glowing skin and hair.

fruit tart

Ingredients

Crust
½ cup refined flour, sifted
¾ cup wholewheat flour, sifted
⅔ cup sugar
½ cup unsweetened cocoa powder
¼ teaspoon salt
150 grams unsalted butter, frozen +
for greasing

Filling
½ cup orange jelly
½ tablespoon fresh lemon juice
1 cup whipping cream
350 grams mixed fruits (canned),
chopped

Method

❶ Grease an eleven-inch diameter springform tart
pan with butter.

❷ Preheat an oven to 180°C/350°F/Gas Mark 4.

❸ In a food processor, mix together both types of
flour, sugar, cocoa powder and salt and blend
for five seconds.

❹ Cut the butter into small pieces, add and blend till
you get a moist sandy texture.

❺ Add one-and-a-half tablespoons of chilled water
and blend until the dough comes together.

❻ Press evenly onto the bottom and up the sides
of the prepared pan and prick it all over with a fork.
Refrigerate for thirty minutes.

❼ Blind bake the crust for around fifteen minutes in
the preheated oven or until it looks dry and slightly
puffed up. Remove from the oven and set aside to cool.

❽ For the filling, melt the orange jelly with lemon
juice and brush a thin layer over the base of the tart.
Whip the cream and spread a thin layer over the jelly.
Arrange the fruits on top and brush with the jelly glaze.

❾ Cut into wedges and serve immediately.

Chef's Tip: Fruit tart can be made into individual
bite-sized pieces also. Roll, cut and line individual
tartlet moulds and do the same as for the big tart.

Blind baking is a technique wherein the crust of a pastry
(i.e. pies, tarts) is partially or completely baked before
it is filled. Line the pie dish with the pastry, prick it with
a fork all over and bake. Or place a greaseproof paper
over the pastry, place some kidney beans over it and
bake. This is to ensure that the pastry does not rise and
remains flat.

orange and chocochip muffins

Ingredients

1½ cups refined flour
1 teaspoon orange rind, chopped
½ cup orange juice
½ cup chocolate chips
1½ teaspoons baking powder
½ teaspoon baking soda
¾ cup powdered sugar
2 tablespoons cocoa powder
¼ teaspoon salt
1 egg
A few drops vanilla essence
½ cup buttermilk
½ cup butter, melted

Method

❶ Preheat an oven to 180°C/350°F/Gas Mark 4. Grease twelve muffin moulds.

❷ Sift the flour, baking powder, baking soda, powdered sugar, cocoa powder and salt into a large bowl. Mix well.

❸ Break the egg into another bowl and whisk lightly. Add the orange rind and whisk some more. Add the vanilla essence and mix. Add the buttermilk and mix again. Add the melted butter and whisk well. Add the orange juice and mix again.

❹ Add the mixture to the flour mixture and mix well. Add half the chocolate chips and mix.

❺ Pour into the prepared muffin moulds and sprinkle the remaining chocolate chips on top.

❻ Place the moulds in the preheated oven and bake for twenty to thirty minutes.

❼ Remove from the oven and let them rest for about ten minutes. Unmould and serve warm.

Young children love having finger foods or 'pick-me-up' foods like these muffins... an excellent way to initiate their liking for fruits and fruity flavours.

aamras with kesar

Ingredients

1 kilogram ripe mangoes
¼ teaspoon saffron threads, roasted and crushed
1 cup sugar, powdered
2½ cups skimmed milk, chilled

Method

❶ Exract the pulp from the mangoes. Pass through a thin piece of muslin.

❷ Add the powdered sugar and chilled milk.

❸ Stir in the saffron.

❹ Serve chilled.

Come summer time, mangoes dominate the scene! *Aamras* is an all-time favourite and originates in the western states of the country. Mangoes are recommended - they are high in Vitamin A, Vitamin E and selenium – as they are heart-healthy.

gajar aur khajur ka halwa

Ingredients

8-10 medium carrots, grated
¾ cup dates, seeded and chopped
1 tablespoon olive oil
½ cup sugar
2 cups skimmed milk
½ cup crumbled *khoya/mawa*
4-5 cashew nuts, roughly chopped
½ teaspoon green cardamom powder
10-12 almonds, blanched and slivered

Method

❶ Heat the olive oil in a *kadai*. Add the grated carrots and sugar and cook for about five minutes.

❷ Add the milk and continue to cook for six to eight minutes.

❸ Add the *khoya*, dates, cashew nuts and green cardamom powder and mix. Cook for ten to fifteen minutes or till almost dry.

❹ Serve hot, garnished with almond slivers.

Pick the long, thin, very red, juicy and sweet carrots for best results. And for a healthier variation add dates. Dates are easily digested, are rich in iron and give this all-time favourite dish a very interesting texture.

date and anjeer baked karanji

Ingredients

Covering
½ cup wholewheat flour
½ cup refined flour
2 tablespoons semolina
2 tablespoons pure ghee + to brush
¼ cup skimmed milk

Filling
¾ cup chopped seedless dates
¾ cup dried figs, chopped
15-20 almonds, crushed
7-8 cashew nuts, crushed
7-8 pistachios, crushed
1 teaspoon green cardamom powder
1 tablespoon roasted poppy seeds
2 tablespoons skimmed milk

Method

❶ For the covering, place the wholewheat flour andrefined flour in a bowl. Add the semolina, two tablespoons ghee and milk and knead intoa semi-soft dough. Divide into equal portions and shape them into *pedas*. Keep them covered with a damp cloth.

❷ Preheat the oven to 180°C/350°F/Gas Mark 4.

❸ To make the filling, place the dates and figs in a bowl. Add the almonds, cashew nuts, pistachios, cardamom powder, poppy seeds and mix. Mash lightly with fingers and add a little milk.

❹ Roll out a dough *peda*. Place it in the *karanji* mould. Place a small portion of the prepared filling in the hollow. Apply a little water on the edges, close the mould and press firmly.

❺ Remove the excess dough and use again. Similarly prepare the remaining *karanjis*.

❻ The *karanjis* can be made without the mould too.

❼ Place the *karanjis* on a greased baking tray. Brush them with a little ghee and bake in the preheated oven for twenty to twenty-five minutes. Cool and store in an airtight container.

There are some *mithai* that have to be deep-fried: for example *jalebis* and *gulab jamuns*. But there are some *mithai* that take well to baking and this is one of them! The wholewheat flour contains thiamine, riboflavin, niacin and iron thus making these *karanjis* healthy. Dried figs are high in insoluble fibre.

zafrani sevian

Ingredients

6 tablespoons vermicelli
10-15 saffron threads
7½ cups (1½ litres) skimmed milk
8 tablespoons sugar
20 raisins
1 teaspoon green cardamom powder
1 tablespoon toasted almond slivers

Method

❶ Heat a non-stick pan and roast the vermicelli on medium heat till lightly browned.

❷ Bring the milk to a boil in a deep pan. Lower the heat and simmer for two to three minutes.
❸ Add the sugar and cook till it dissolves. Add the vermicelli and raisins and cook for two minutes.

❹ Take it off the heat. Add the saffron and cardamom powder and stir well.

❺ Serve hot or cold, garnished with toasted almond slivers.

Vermicelli made from wholewheat is a rich source of protein and carbohydrate. Growing children need extra energy and this sweet is ideal for them.

yogurt and chiku ice cream

Ingredients

1 cup drained skimmed milk yogurt
6 medium *chikus*
¼ cup powdered sugar
3 tablespoons honey
½ cup condensed milk
8-10 walnut kernels, crushed

Method

❶ Peel and pit the *chikus*. Place them in a processor/mixer and crush.

❷ Add the drained yogurt and powdered sugar and mix. Add the honey and process again.

❸ Add the condensed milk and mix. Finally add the crushed walnuts and mix.

❹ Transfer the mixture into an ice cream tin and level the top.

❺ Place the tin in the deep freezer to set.

❻ When firmly set, scoop out into individual bowls and serve.

Skimmed milk yogurt is an excellent alternative to fresh cream. It adds protein and Vitamin C and reduces fat. *Chiku* is high in complex carbohydrates, calcium and iron. This ice cream can be enjoyed by growing children for it is not only tasty but nutritious too.

very low-fat brownies

Ingredients

3 tablespoons unsweetened cocoa powder
½ cup wholewheat flour
½ cup refined flour
½ teaspoon baking powder
½ teaspoon soda bicarbonate
1 cup caster sugar
½ cup skimmed milk
2 egg whites, beaten
1 teaspoon vanilla essence
1½ tablespoons oil

Method

❶ Preheat an oven to 180°C/350°F/Gas Mark 4. Line an eight-inch square cake tin with butter paper.

❷ Sift the cocoa powder, wholewheat flour, refined flour, baking powder and soda bicarbonate into a bowl.

❸ Stir in the caster sugar, then beat in the milk, egg whites, vanilla essence and oil until thoroughly combined.

❹ Pour the mixture into the prepared tin.

❺ Bake in the preheated oven for about twenty-five minutes or until just firm to the touch. Leave in the tin until completely cooled.

❻ Using a sharp knife, cut into sixteen squares, then remove from the tin using a spatula.

Low-fat brownies are a dieter's treat! They can be given to growing children also. Eggs provide good quality protein, calcium and Vitamins A and B.

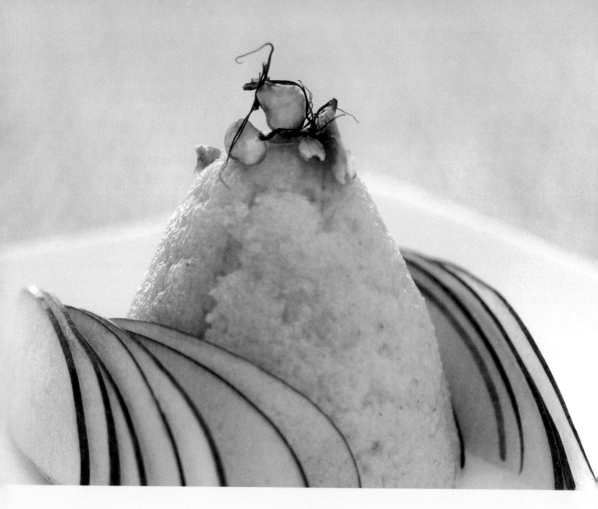

saeb aur sooji halwa

Ingredients

2 large apples, thinly sliced
+ 1 large apple, puréed
½ cup semolina
1 cup skimmed milk
⅓ cup sugar
½ teaspoon green cardamom powder
A generous pinch of saffron
5-6 pistachios, blanched and slivered

Method

❶ Dry-roast the semolina lightly, taking care that it does not change colour.

❷ Boil the milk with one cup of water in a deep pan. Add the sugar, cardamom powder and half of the saffron.

❸ Slowly add the semolina and cook, stirring, till it becomes semi-dry. Add the puréed apple. Cook for two to three minutes.

❹ Divide into four portions. Pack each portion tightly into a bowl, turn it upside down onto a serving plate and de-mould.

❺ Decorate with apple slices, pistachios and saffron.

A comforting dish for a cold winter's day. The best part is that unlike traditional *halwas* this is easy to make even without added fat! Apples add fibre and phytonutrients.

annexure

chutneys

Kolhapuri Dry Chutney

Dry-roast 1 cup coriander seeds, 1 tablespoon cumin seeds, 1 tablespoon sesame seeds, 8-10 black peppercorns, ½-inch cinnamon stick, 10 cloves and 1 teaspoon fennel seeds. Set aside to cool. Roast ½ cup grated dried coconut till lightly browned. Set aside to cool. Heat 2 tablespoons oil and fry 2 roughly-chopped medium onions, 10 garlic cloves and 1 cup chopped fresh coriander on low heat till well browned and crisp. Set aside to cool. Mix all these and grind to a fine powder. Mix with 1 cup red chilli powder. Store when completely cooled in an air-tight container preferably in a refrigerator.

Mint Chutney

Grind 3 cups of chopped fresh mint, 2 cups of fresh coriander, 6 chopped green chillies, 1 medium onion chopped and 3-inch piece of ginger to a fine paste adding a little water if required. Add 2 tablespoons lemon juice, salt and 2 tablespoons of dried pomegranate seed powder.
Mix well and serve.

Date and Tamarind Chutney

Wash, stone and chop 15-20 dates. Dry-roast 2 teaspoons cumin seeds and ¼ teaspoon fennel seeds. Cool and grind to a powder. Cook the dates, 1 cup tamarind pulp, cumin and fennel powder, ½ cup jaggery, 2 teaspoons red chilli powder, 1 teaspoon dried ginger powder, black salt, salt and four cups of water till thick.

Pineapple Chutney

Peel and cut 1 medium pineapple into small pieces and place in a thick-bottomed pan. Add 1 teaspoon ginger paste, mix well and cook for 5 minutes. Add 1 tablespoon sugar and 2 tablespoons raisins and cook. Add ½ teaspoon roasted *panch phoron* powder, ½ teaspoon crushed red chillies and salt to taste. Add ½ cup water and cook for 5 minutes on low heat. Sprinkle ½ teaspoon roasted *panch phoron* powder and serve.

Note: *Panch phoron* is a mixture of ¼ teaspoon mustard seeds, ¼ teaspoon cumin seeds, ¼ teaspoon fenugreek seeds, ¼ teaspoon fennel seeds and ¼ teaspoon onion seeds.

stock

Chicken Stock

Place 200 grams blanched chicken bones, 1 medium quartered onion, 1 medium roughly chopped carrot, 1 stalk chopped celery, 2-3 stalks chopped parsley, 1 chopped leek with leek leaves, 6-7 black peppercorns, 5-6 cloves and 1 bay leaf in a deep pan with 10 cups of water and heat. Bring the mixture to a boil, remove any scum which comes on the top, and replace it with more cold water. Simmer the stock for a minimum period of 1 hour. Remove from heat, strain, cool and store in a refrigerator till needed. Unutilised chicken carcass (neck, winglets, bones etc.) can be used to make this stock.

Fish Stock

Place 200 grams fish bones, head, skin and any unutilised portions of fish, in a pan with 5 cups of water, 1 medium onion sliced, 1 large fresh button mushroom sliced, 2-3 inch stalk celery chopped fine, 1 bay leaf and 4-6 black peppercorns. Bring to a boil, remove any scum which rises to the surface and simmer for 15 minutes. Remove from heat and strain. Discard the solids and use immediately. If storing in a refrigerator, do so in an air-tight container so that the other items in the refrigerator do not get the fishy smell.

Vegetable Stock

Place 1 medium chopped onion, ½ medium chopped carrot, 2-3 inches celery stalk chopped, 2 crushed garlic cloves, 1 bay leaf, 5-6 black peppercorns and 2-3 cloves in a pan with 5 cups of water and bring it to a boil. Simmer for 15 minutes and strain. Cool and store in a refrigerator till further use.

Mutton Stock

Wash and clean 200 grams of mutton bones, removing any excess fat. Boil in water to cover for 5 minutes. Drain and discard the liquid. Boil blanched bones, 1 chopped onion, 1 carrot, cut into large pieces, 1 stalk of celery and 2-3 stalks of parsley, both cut into 2-3 inch pieces, 6-7 black peppercorns and 1 bay leaf in a deep pan with 10 cups of water. Simmer for at least 1 hour, removing any scum which rises to the top. Strain and use as required.

others

Skimmed Milk Cottage Cheese (Paneer)

Bring 5 cups or 1 litre skimmed milk to a boil. Add 2 tablespoons lemon juice or vinegar and continue to boil, stirring continuously, and allow the milk to curdle. Strain the curdled milk through a piece of muslin and tie it up tightly in a bag or *potli*. Once most of the water drains away, place the *potli* under a heavy weight like a grinding stone (*paat*), for 4 to 5 hours. When all the water has drained away, the cottage cheese or *paneer* will form a solid mass. Cut into cubes and use as required. Store it for not more than two days in a refrigerator. This recipe will yield 200 grams of cottage cheese.
Note: For *malai paneer* use full-cream milk and follow the same procedure.

Coconut Milk

Process 1 cup grated fresh coconut with ¼ cup warm water in a blender. Strain the ground coconut through a piece of muslin or strainer to extract the thick first milk. Add ¼ cup of warm water to the residue and process again to extract the second or thinner milk.

Massaman Curry Paste

Cook 4 finely chopped spring onions, 12 chopped garlic cloves, 1-inch chopped galangal, 1 chopped lemon grass stalk, 2 cloves, 1 tablespoon coriander seeds and 1 teaspoon cumin seeds in a wok on low heat for 5 minutes. Grind to a paste. Add 5 black peppercorns, 3 dried red chillies and 1 teaspoon salt and grind again. Add 1 teaspoon shrimp paste and mix well. This will make half a cup of curry paste.

Salsa

Crush 4 garlic cloves and chop 1 small onion. Heat 1½ tablespoons oil in a pan and sauté the garlic and onion. Add 2 fresh chopped red chillies, ½ small green capsicum, chopped, ½ teaspoon roasted cumin powder, 1 teaspoon red chilli powder and 1 cup tomato purée. Stir well and add salt to taste. Cook for 2 to 3 minutes and remove from heat. When cool, stir in 1 tablespoon lemon juice and 2 tablespoons chopped fresh coriander.

Boiled Onion Paste

Peel and roughly chop 4-5 medium onions. Place in a pan and add 1 bay leaf, 1 black cardamom and ½ cup water. Bring to a boil and simmer until the onions are transparent and the liquid has evaporated. Cool, and then discard the bay leaf and cardamom. Transfer the onions to a blender and process to a fine paste.

Chilli Oil

Cook 6 tablespoons of chopped dried red chillies in 1¼ cups of groundnut oil, on low heat, for at least 10 minutes. When completely cold, stir in 2-3 tablespoons of red chilli powder and 1-2 tablespoons of sesame oil. Cover and leave to stand for at least 12 hours. Strain into a sterilised bottle and store in a cool, dark place.

Potli Masala

Mix 200 grams coriander seeds, 25 grams sandalwood powder, 35 grams dried vetiver roots (*khus*), 35 grams bay leaves, 20 grams dried rose petals, 25 grams black cardamoms, 30 grams cassia buds, 15 grams cinnamon, 30 grams lichen/stone flower *(patthar phool)*, 35 grams *kulanjan (paan ki jad)* and 25 grams *kapur kachri* and store in an airtight jar. When required, tie a small amount in a piece of muslin and add it to the water to be used for cooking.

White Sauce

Melt 2 tablespoons of butter in a heavy-bottomed pan and stir in 2 tablespoons refined flour. Cook for 5 to 6 minutes over low heat till fragrant. Stir in 2 cups milk and whisk till smooth. Cook for 4 to 5 minutes, stirring continuously, till the sauce thickens. Add salt to taste and ½ teaspoon white pepper powder and mix well. Strain the sauce. Makes 2 cups

Variations

Cream sauce: Add ¼ cup of cream and 2 tablespoons of melted butter to the white sauce.
Parsley sauce: Add 1 tablespoon of chopped parsley to the cream sauce.

glossary

English	Hindi	English	Hindi
Almonds	Badam	Black salt	Kala namak
Alum	Phitkari	Blueberries	Falsa
Amaranth	Chouli/Chavli	Boneless chicken	Murgh boti
Aniseed	Saunf	Boneless mutton	Gosht boti
Apple	Saeb	Bottle gourd	Lauki/Ghia/Doodhi
Apricot	Khubani	Bread	Double roti
Arrowroot	Paniphal, Tikora	Brinjal	Baingan
Artichoke	Hathichak	Broad beans	Papdi
Asafoetida	Hing	Broccoli florets	Hari phoolgobhi
Ash gourd	Petha	Broken wheat	Dalia
Asparagus	Shatawari	Browned onion	Bhuna pyaaz
Aubergine/ Eggplant/Brinjal	Baingan	Buckwheat	Kootoo
Avocado	Makhanphal		
		Cabbage	Pattagobhi
Baby brinjals	Chhote baingan	Camphor	Kapur
Baby potatoes	Chhote aloo	Caraway seeds	Shahi jeera
Banana	Kela	Carom seeds	Ajwain
Banana leaf	Kele ka patta	Carrots	Gajar
Barley	Jau	Cashew nuts	Kaju
Basmati rice	Basmati chawal	Cauliflower	Phoolgobhi
Bay leaf	Tej patta	Celery	Ajmud
Bean curd	Tofu	Cherry tomatoes	Chhote tamatar
Bean sprouts	Ankurit moong	Chicken	Murgh
Beetroot	Chukandar	Chicken breasts	Murgh ka seena
Bengal gram	Chana	Chicken mince	Murgh keema
Berries	Ker	Chicken wings and shoulder	Murgh pankhari
Betel leaf	Paan	Chickpeas	Kabuli chana
Betel nut	Supari	Cinnamon	Dalchini
Bitter gourd	Karela	Citric acid	Tartri
Black Bengal gram	Kale chane	Cloves	Laung
Black cardamoms	Badi elaichi	Cluster beans	Gwar
Black-eyed beans	Lobia	Cobra saffron	Nagkeshar
Black grapes	Kale angoor	Coconut	Nariyal
Black olives	Kala jaitun	Colocasia	Arbi
Black peppercorns	Kali mirch	Colocasia leaves	Arbi ke patte

English	Hindi	English	Hindi
Coriander powder	Dhania powder	Flattened rice	Poha/Chewra
Coriander seeds	Dhania	Flax seeds/Linseed	Alsi
Corn kernels	Makai ke dane	French beans	Farsi
Cornmeal	Makai ka atta	Fresh basil	Tulsi
Cottage cheese	Paneer	Fresh coriander	Hara dhania
Crab	Kekda	Fresh cream	Malai
Cucumber	Kakdi/Kheera	Fresh mint	Pudina
Cumin seeds	Jeera	Fresh parsely	Ajmoda
Curry leaves	Kadhi patta/Meetha neem	Fresh pomegranate kernels	Anaar ke dane
		Fresh red chillies	Tazi lal mirch
Custard apple	Sharifa/Sitaphal	Fresh turmeric	Tazi haldi
Dates	Khajur	Garlic	Lehsun
Dill	Suva	Ginger	Adrak
Dried beans	Sangri	Gram flour	Besan
Dried coconut	Khopra	Grapes	Angoor
Dried dates	Chuare	Green capsicum	Hari Shimla mirch
Dried fenugreek leaves	Kasoori methi	Green cardamoms	Chhoti elaichi
Dried fruits	Sukha Mewa	Green chillies	Hari mirch
Dried ginger powder	Saunth	Green gram dumplings	Mangodi
Dried mango powder	Amchur	Green peas	Matar
Dried pomegranate seeds	Anardana	Guavas	Amrud
Dried red chillies	Sookhi lal mirch		
Drumsticks	Saijan ki Phalli		
		Honey	Shahad/Madhu
		Horse gram	Koolith
Egg	Anda	Hung (drained) yogurt	Chakka
Egg white	Ande ki safedi		
Egg yolk	Zardi		
		Iceberg lettuce	Salad ke Patte
		Indian gooseberry	Amla
Fennel seeds	Saunf	Indian salmon	Rawas
Fenugreek leaves	Methi	Ivy gourd	Tindora/Tondli
Fenugreek seeds	Methi dana		
Fig	Anjeer		
Finger millet	Ragi/Nachni	Jackfruit	Kathal
		Jaggery	Gur

English	Hindi	English	Hindi
Kidney beans	Rajma	Oats	Jav
King fish	Surmai	Onion seeds	Kalonji
Kohl rabi	Ganth gobi/	Onions	Pyaaz
	Navalkol	Orange	Narangi/Santra
Ladies' fingers	Bhindi	Papaya	Papita
Lamb leg	Raan	Parboiled rice	Ukda chawal
Leek	Bilayti pyaaz	Peaches	Aadoo
Lemon grass stalk	Chai ki patti	Peanuts/ground nuts	Moongphali
Lemon rind	Nimboo ka chilka	Pear	Naspati
Lemon	Nimboo	Pickle	Achaar
Lotus leaves	Kamal ke pate	Pigeon peas	Sabut toovar/
Lotus roots	Kamal kakdi/Bhen		Sabut arhar
		Pineapple	Annanas
		Pine nuts	Chilgoza
Mace	Javitri	Pistachio	Pista
Mackerel	Bangda	Plums	Aloobukara
Mango	Aam	Pomfret	Halva/Saranga/
Mango pulp	Aam ka guda		Chandwa/Poplait
Milk	Doodh	Pomegranate	Anar
Millet	Bajra	Poppy seeds	Khuskhus
Millet flour	Bajre ka atta	Potatoes	Aloo
Minced meat	Keema	Powdered sugar	Pisi hui cheeni
Mushrooms	Kukurmutta/Gucchi/	Prawns	Jheenga
	Dhingri/Khumb	Prunes	Sookhe adu
Musk melon	Kharbooj	Puffed rice	Murmura
Mussels/clams	Shevma	Pure ghee	Desi ghee
Mustard oil	Rai ka tel/Sarson		
	ka tel		
Mustard seeds	Rai/Sarson	Radish	Mooli
Mutton	Gosht	Raisins	Kishmish
Mutton chops	Champen	Raw bananas	Kachche kele
		Raw mangoes	Keri
		Red button chillies	Boria mirch
Nutmeg	Jaiphal	Red cabbage	Lal gobhi

English	Hindi	English	Hindi
Red capsicum	Lal Shimla mirch	Star fruit/Karambola	Kamrak
Red pumpkin	Kaddu	Stone flower	Dagad phool
Refined flour	Maida	Stone apple/Passion fruit	Bael phal
Rice	Chawal		
Ridge gourd	Turai	Sugarcane	Ganna
Roasted chana dal	Daalia	Sweet lime	Moosambi
Rock salt	Sendha namak	Sweet potato	Shakkarkand/Rattalu
Rose water	Gulab jal	Sweetcorn kernels	Makai ke dane
Saffron	Kesar	Tamarind	Imli
Sago	Sabudana	Tea leaves	Chai ki pattiyan
Salt	Namak	Tomatoes	Tamatar
Sambhar onions/Shallots	Chhote pyaaz	Turmeric powder	Haldi powder
Sandalwood	Chandan	Turnip	Shalgam
Sapodila/Sapota	Chickoo		
Screwpine	Kewra		
Sea salt	Samudri namak	Vetiver	Khus
Semolina	Rawa/Sooji	Vinegar	Sirka
Sesame seeds	Til		
Snake gourd	Padwal/Chichinda		
Soda bicarbonate	Meetha soda	Walnut	Akhrot
Sorghum	Jowar	Water chestnut	Singhara
Split Bengal gram	Chana dal	Watermelon	Tarbooja
Split black gram skinless	Dhuli urad dal	Wheat	Gehun
Split black gram with skin	Chilkewali urad dal	White radishes	Safed mooli
Split coriander seeds	Dhania dal	White vinegar	Safed sirka
Split fenugreek seeds	Methi dal	Whole black gram	Sabut urad
Split green gram skinless	Dhuli moong dal	Whole green gram	Sabut moong
Split green gram with skin	Chilkewali moong dal	Whole red lentils	Sabut masoor
Split lentils	Masoor dal	Wholewheat flour	Atta
Split mustard seeds	Rai dal		
Split pigeon peas	Toovar dal/Arhar dal		
Spinach	Palak	Yam	Zamikand/Suran
Spring onion	Hara pyaaz	Yeast	Khameer
Spring onion greens	Hare pyaaz ki pattiyan	Yellow capsicum	Pili Shimla mirch
Sprouted green gram	Ankurit moong	Yogurt	Dahi
Star anise	Chakri phool/Badiyan	Zucchini	Tori/Turaii